96 Kidney Stone Preventing Meal and Juice Recipes:

Using Smart Nutrition to Reduce Your Chances to Having Kidney Stones

By

Joe Correa CSN

COPYRIGHT

This publication is designed to provide accurate and authoritative information in regard to the subject matter covered. It is sold with the understanding that neither the author nor the publisher is engaged in rendering medical advice. If medical advice or assistance is needed, consult with a doctor. This book is considered a guide and should not be used in any way detrimental to your health. Consult with a physician before starting this nutritional plan to make sure it's right for you.

ACKNOWLEDGEMENTS

This book is dedicated to my friends and family that have had mild or serious illnesses so that you may find a solution and make the necessary changes in your life.

96 Kidney Stone Preventing Meal and Juice Recipes:

Using Smart Nutrition to Reduce Your Chances to Having Kidney Stones

By

Joe Correa CSN

CONTENTS

ABOUT THE AUTHOR

After years of Research, I honestly believe in the positive effects that proper nutrition can have over the body and mind. My knowledge and experience has helped me live healthier throughout the years and which I have shared with family and friends. The more you know about eating and drinking healthier, the sooner you will want to change your life and eating habits.

Nutrition is a key part in the process of being healthy and living longer so get started today. The first step is the most important and the most significant.

INTRODUCTION

96 Kidney Stone Preventing Meal and Juice Recipes: Using Smart Nutrition to Reduce Your Chances to Having Kidney Stones

By Joe Correa CSN

Kidney stones are serious and very painful. If you have never experienced kidney stones than you saved yourself the discomfort. These meal and juice recipes are not only mouthwatering but are also packed with essential nutrients that our body needs to help prevent the formation of kidney stones and even help break them down.

Most kidney stones are created when the urine becomes concentrated with crystal-forming substances such as calcium, oxalate, sodium, phosphorous, and uric acid. To counteract these stone promoters, several factors present in the urine act to inhibit stone formation. The factors include: amount of urine excreted, the amounts of citrate, magnesium, pyrophosphate, phytate, and other proteins and molecules that are derived from normal metabolism. These inhibitors help eliminate crystals before they attach to the kidney walls and grow into larger stones.

Kidney stones can be prevented by drinking a lot of fluid. Including citrus beverages in your diet increases citrate levels in the body. Citrate helps by blocking the formation of stones. Getting too little calcium can cause oxalate levels to rise and cause kidney stones. A diet rich in calcium is beneficial, while vitamin D helps the body absorb calcium properly. A high-protein diet increases the level of uric acid that can promote kidney stone formation. A high-salt diet should also be avoided. Lastly foods high in oxalates and phosphates such as chocolate, coffee, and tea should be avoided.

Don't wait to have kidney stones. Prevent or eliminate them using these delicious recipes. Make sure to try them all so that you can find your favorite ones.

Avoid:
high protein
sodium
chocolate
coffee
tea

Add to diet:
citrus
calcium
vit D

96 KIDNEY STONE PREVENTING MEAL AND JUICE RECIPES: USING SMART NUTRITION TO REDUCE YOUR CHANCES TO HAVING KIDNEY STONES

MEALS

1.   Broc-Coli stir-fry

A half cup of broccoli contains a little more than 20 mg of calcium. It is also rich in vitamin C which can help promote liver detoxification. Broccoli is also rich in potassium, iron, magnesium, zinc, protein, carbohydrate and other vitamins.

Ingredients:

1 cup Broccoli

½ cup Cauliflower

½ cup Red bell pepper

100 g. Leftover chicken, shredded

1 Tbsp. Onion, chopped

1 Tbsp. Garlic, chopped

Procedure:

Over medium heat, sauté garlic until brown and onion

becomes translucent. Add the shredded chicken, stir for one minute or until evenly brown. Throw in all vegetables and cook until broccoli is dark green and red bell pepper has slightly wilted. Remove from fire and transfer to a plate.

Amount Per Serving:

Serves: 1 • Serving size: 305 g

Calories 217

Total Fat 4.0g, Cholesterol 73mg

Sodium 106mg, potassium 1006mg

Total carbohydrates 15.2g, sugars 5.2g

Protein30.8 g

Vitamin A 40% • Vitamin C 277% • Calcium 8% • Iron 13%

2.   Stir-fried bok choy with shrimp

Bok choy contains powerful antioxidants like vitamins C and A, and phytonutrients such as sulforaphane that significantly improves kidney function. Its phytonutrients stimulate detoxifying enzymes that help prevent cancers of the prostate, breast and colon. It is rich in dietary fiber, vitamins B, B1, B5, B6 and folate.

Ingredients

1 cup Bok choy, chopped

1 Tbsp. Onion, chopped

1 Tbsp. Garlic, chopped

1 Tbsp. Olive oil

¼ cup Shrimp, peeled and deveined

Preparation:

Over medium heat, sauté garlic until brown and onion becomes translucent. Add the shrimp, cook until bright pink. Throw in the bok choy. Cook until bok choy is dark green. Serve on a dish and enjoy.

Amount Per Serving:

Serves: 1 • Serving size: 103 g

Calories 146

Total Fat 14.2g, Cholesterol 0mg

Sodium 47mg, potassium 225mg

Total carbohydrates 5.2g, sugars 1.3g

Protein 1.7g

Vitamin A 63% • Vitamin C 58% • Calcium 9% • Iron 4%

3. Red and yellow bell pepper chicken fajita

Bell pepper contains high amounts of vitamins A and C and is very low in potassium making this vegetable very friendly to the kidney. Best of all it increases patients' appetite due to its ability to stimulate the secretion of saliva and gastric juice.

Ingredients:

200g. Chicken strips

1 Tbsp. Onion, chopped

1/4 cup Yellow bell pepper, minced

¼ cup Red bell pepper, minced

2 tsp. Olive oil

1 Pocket fajita

1 Tbsp. Sour cream

½ tsp. Paprika

Preparation:

In a skillet, over medium heat, sauté the onion in olive oil until translucent. Add the chicken strips and stir-fry until thoroughly cooked, or until 2-3 minutes. Add the peppers and cook for a while. Stir until bell peppers have slightly softened. Season with paprika, stir and remove from heat.

In a separate small bowl, transfer the chicken mixture and stir in the sour cream. Scoop into a pocket fajita and enjoy!

Amount per Serving:

Serves: 1 • Serving size: 278 g

Calories 446

Total Fat 18.3g, Cholesterol 187mg

Sodium 266mg, potassium 637mg

Total carbohydrates 4.2g, sugars 2.4g

Protein 65.3g

Vitamin A 33% • Vitamin C 99% • Calcium 5% • Iron 16%

4.   Cantaloupe cucumber and mango smoothie

Cantaloupe is rich in antioxidants, vitamins A and C, which stimulate white blood cells to counteract the weakening immune system caused by kidney disease. It also improves anemia, controls diabetes and alleviates arthritis.

Ingredients:

1 cup Cantaloupe, chopped

½ cup Cucumber, chopped

¾ cup Mango, chopped

1 cup Plain low-fat yogurt

Preparation:

Throw in all ingredients in a blender. Blend well and transfer to chilled glasses.

Amount Per Serving:

 Serves: 2 • Serving size: 277 g

Calories 118

Total Fat 1.7g, Cholesterol m7g

Sodium 99mg, potassium 533mg

Total carbohydrates 15.9g, sugars 15.2g

Protein 7.8g

Vitamin A 55% • Vitamin C 51% • Calcium 24% • Iron 2%

5.   Chicken papaya soup

Papaya is a powerhouse of various nutrients and vitamins. It is rich in antioxidants, phytochemicals, vitamins A, C, B Complex and folates. It is low in sodium, high in potassium, and rich in digestive enzymes.

Ingredients:

2 cups Green papaya, thinly sliced

200 g Ground chicken

4 cups Chicken broth

1 Tbsp. Onion

1 tsp. Ginger, minced

Preparation:

In a pot, over medium heat, sauté the onion until translucent. Stir in the ginger and the ground chicken. Cook until ginger is dark yellow and the ground chicken is slightly cooked, or for about a minute or two. Add the chicken broth and the green papaya. Simmer for 5 minutes or until green papaya is soft.

Amount Per Serving:

Serves: 6 • Serving size: 242g

Calories 110

Total Fat 3.5 g, Cholesterol 30mg

Sodium 542mg, potassium 309mg

Total carbohydrates 6.0g, sugars 4.3g

Protein 13.1g

Vitamin A 10% • Vitamin C 49% • Calcium 2% • Iron 5%

6.   Baked banana fritters

A diet high in calcium, low in potassium and low in magnesium can cause calcium to contribute to kidney stone formation. Bananas contain very little calcium and high levels of magnesium and potassium.

Ingredients:

2 Bananas, cut into ¾ "

1 Egg white

1/3 cup Bread crumbs

¾ cup Honey

Olive oil for greasing

Preparation:

Preheat oven to 350 F.

Combine bread crumbs, honey and egg white in a bowl. Beat until well blended and frothy. Dip each banana slice into the mixture. Place the breaded bananas on a greased baking sheet and bake for 10 minutes or until bananas are brown.

Amount Per Serving:

Serves: 3 • Serving size: 102 g

Calories 123

Total Fat 0.9g, Cholesterol 0mg

Sodium 100mg, potassium 323mg

Total carbohydrates 26.7 g, sugars 10.4g

Protein 3.7g

Vitamin A 1% • Vitamin C 11% • Calcium 3% • Iron 4%

7.   Mixed garden greens with apple cider vinaigrette

Apple cider vinegar is a known and effective way to eliminate kidney stones due to its high

acidity level that breaks down the hard tissues that form the kidney stones. Hence, stones are made to pass easily through urine.

Ingredients:

1/4 cup Apple cider vinegar

¼ cup. Honey

1 cup Olive oil

4 cups Loosely packed romaine lettuce

½ cup Feta cheese

Preparation:

In a medium-sized bowl, combine apple cider vinegar, honey and olive oil. Stir then toss in all remaining ingredients.

Amount Per Serving:

 Serves: 4 • Serving size: 143 g

Calories 492

Total Fat 54.5g, Cholesterol 17mg

Sodium 213mg, potassium 100mg

Total carbohydrates 2.6g, sugars 1.4g

Protein 2.9g

Vitamin A 2% • Vitamin C 4 % • Calcium 9% • Iron 9%

8.   Lemon cucumber basil sorbet

Lime juice raises acidity, citrate and potassium levels while increasing the urine output without increasing calcium content, thereby preventing calcium crystal formation that can develop into kidney stone.

Ingredients:

4 Fresh basil

¼ cup Lime juice

1 Cucumber, chopped

½ cup Honey

1 cup Water

Preparation:

Blend cucumber in a food processor. Add the basil and lime juice. Puree with remaining half cup of water. Then add the honey and water. Leave mix in freezer for 20 minutes or until semi-frozen. After 25 minutes, blend again until ice is crystal fine. Refreeze until ready to be consumed.

Amount Per Serving:

Serves: 2 • Serving size: 269g.

Calories 23

Total Fat 0.2g, Cholesterol 0mg

Sodium 7mg, potassium 222mg

Total carbohydrates 5.5g, sugars 2.5g

Protein 1.0g

Vitamin A 3% • Vitamin C 7% • Calcium 3% • Iron 2%

9.　Dandelion with grilled cheese sandwich

Dandelions contain high doses of iron, zinc, magnesium, phosphate and vitamins A, C, D and B- Complex. The root of dandelion supports liver and gallbladder function. Its leaves, on the other hand have a mild diuretic effect which help eliminate waste products.

Ingredients:

½ cup Mozzarella cheese

1 tsp. Olive oil

Onion

2 slices Whole wheat bread

¼ cup Dandelion leaves, chopped

Preparation:

In a skillet, over medium heat, heat olive oil and place sandwich on pan with cheese on top. Layer the onions and dandelion leaves on top. Lower the heat and cover the sandwich with the top slice until the cheese melts. When bread is brown enough, flip the bread. Transfer to a plate and enjoy!

Amount Per Serving:

Serves: 2 • Serving size: 109 g

Calories 120

Total Fat 3.2 g, Cholesterol 6mg

Sodium 184mg, potassium 150mg

Total carbohydrates 16.9g, sugars 3.9g

Protein 6.2g

Vitamin A 1% • Vitamin C 6% • Calcium 5% • Iron 4%

10.   Chicken Horsetail soup with onion leaves

Horsetail is very rich in silicone and contains numerous vitamins and minerals such as potassium, manganese, magnesium and many trace minerals. It is used as a diuretic and as an astringent. It is prescribed for the treatment of kidney and bladder disorders.

Ingredients:

¾ cup Horesetail shoots (strobil), chopped

3 cups Vegetable broth

200 g. Shredded chicken

1 Tbsp. Onion

1/8 tsp. Pepper

1 Tbsp. Olive oil

Preparation:

Sauté onion in olive oil over medium heat. Add the shredded chicken, cook for a minute or two. Pour the vegetable broth and add the horsetail shoots. Lower heat and simmer for 4-5 minutes or until shoots are tender yet crisp.

Amount Per Serving:

Serves: 4 • serving size: 236 g

Calories 135

Total Fat 6.0 g, Cholesterol 39mg

Sodium 604mg, potassium 253mg

Total carbohydrates 1.0g, sugars0.6 g

Protein18.2 g

Vitamin A 0% • Vitamin C 0% • Calcium 1% • Iron 5%

11. Basil chicken tomato and cheese pita bread

Basil is a detoxifier and diuretic which helps in the elimination of kidney stones. It reduces uric acid levels in blood and cleanses kidneys. It contains acetic acid and other essential oils that help to break down the stones. Its anti-inflammatory property also helps reduce pain caused by stones.

Ingredients:

2 pieces Pita pockets

1 Large tomato, thinly sliced

100g. Leftover chicken, shredded

1 Tbsp. Fresh basil

80 g. Feta cheese, cubed

1 Tbsp. Olive oil

Preparation:

Mix all ingredients in a bowl and stuff everything inside the pita pockets. Toast the pita pockets and enjoy!

Amount Per Serving:

Serves: 2 • serving size: 190 g

Calories 258

Total Fat 17.2g, Cholesterol 74mg

Sodium 482mg, potassium 338mg

Total carbohydrates 5.2g, sugars 4.0g

Protein 21.0g

Vitamin A 20% • Vitamin C 21% • Calcium 22% • Iron 6%

12.   Chicken and egg sandwich salad

Celery helps to clear the toxins that form kidney stones. It also acts as diuretic which helps with the passing of stone.

Ingredients:

½ cup Celery, minced

½ cup Leftover chicken, shredded

1 leaf Romaine lettuce, cut into half

½ Tbsp. Onion, minced

1 Egg, hardboiled

2 slices Wheat bread

2 Tbsp. Mayonnaise

A pinch of Pepper

Preparation:

Boil the eggs for 8 min. Peel the eggs. Mash when cool.

In a small bowl, combine the celery, leftover chicken, onion, egg, and mayonnaise. Mix until well blended. Place romaine lettuce on top of a slice of bread. Spread chicken with egg mixture on top of the lettuce and cover with another slice of sandwich.

Amount Per Serving:

Serves: 2 • Serving size: 95 g

Calories 163

Total Fat 8.1g, Cholesterol 86mg

Sodium 288mg, potassium 174mg

Total carbohydrates 16.3g, sugars 3.1g

Protein 6.7g

Vitamin A 5% • Vitamin C 2% • Calcium 5% • Iron 7%

13. Brown fried rice with nettle leaf

Nettle leaf is a natural diuretic which helps to keep the water flow constantly through kidneys and bladder. It enhances the benefits of water in the removal of kidney stones.

Ingredients:

1 cup Nettle leaf

½ cup Ground beef

1 cup Brown rice, soaked overnight in water (2:1 water to rice ratio)

2 Tbsp. Garlic

2. Spring onion, thinly sliced

1 Tbsp. Garlic powder

1 Olive oil

Preparation:

Boil the nettle leaves and drain.

In a saucepan, over medium heat, sauté onion and garlic in olive oil. Cook until onion is translucent and garlic is brown. Throw in the ground beef and cook for a minute or two. Then add the drained brown rice, nettle leaves and garlic powder. Pour 3 cups of water. Lower heat, cover the pan with a lid and simmer for 25 minutes. Serve hot.

Amount Per Serving:

 Serves: 2 • Serving size: 123 g

Calories 375

Total Fat 2.6g, Cholesterol 0mg

Sodium 9mg, potassium 376mg

Total carbohydrates 79.3g, sugars 1.4g

Protein 8.6g

Vitamin A 3% • Vitamin C 10% • Calcium 6% • Iron 12%

14.   Pomegranate salad

Pomegranates rich in phytochemicals that protect against heart disease, has anti-inflammatory, anti-cancer properties. Both pomegranate seeds and juice, help prevent kidney stones. It flushes toxins from the body and reduces the acidity levels in the urine.

Ingredients:

2 cups Loosely packed Romaine lettuce

4 Tbsp. Pomegranate juice

4 Tbsp. Extra-virgin olive oil

2 Tbsp. Wine vinegar

Seeds from ½ pomegranate

1 Tbsp. Honey

Preparation:

Whisk all ingredients together in a bowl except for the greens. Pour mixture on top of the Romaine lettuce. Transfer to a platter and serve.

Amount Per Serving:

 Serves: 2 • serving size: 224 g

Calories 303

Total Fat 28.1g, Cholesterol 0mg

Sodium 205mg, potassium 158mg

Total carbohydrates 33.9g, sugars14.2 g

Protein 0.3g

Vitamin A0 % • Vitamin C 8% • Calcium 0% • Iron 9%

15. Shrimp vinaigrette salad

Leafy green vegetables contain a high amount of magnesium. Magnesium helps prevent calcium from combining with oxalate. This inhibits crystal formation thereby reducing the risk of forming kidney stones.

Ingredients:

3 cups Loosely packed mixed greens

1/2 cup Shrimp, peeled and deveined

Dressing:

10 Fresh basil leaves, chopped very finely

4 Tbsp. Olive oil

2 Tbsp. Hot water

1 1/2 tbsp. Apple cider vinegar

A pinch of Pepper

Preparation:

Peel and devein the shrimp. Season with pepper then steam until bright orange. In a medium-sized bowl, combine with greens and set aside.

In a small bowl, combine all ingredients for dressing. Pour on top of the mixed greens with shrimp. Transfer to a plate and serve.

Amount Per Serving:

Serves: 3 • Serving size: 214 g

Calories 279

Total Fat 19.0g, Cholesterol 0mg

Sodium 64mg, potassium 313mg

Total carbohydrates 23.9g, sugars 5.7 g

Protein 5.3g

Vitamin A 157% • Vitamin C 10% • Calcium 5% • Iron 9%

16.   Apricot salad with croutons

Apricots contain high amount of potassium which have been shown to help reduce the chances of getting kidney stones.

Ingredients:

2 apricots, pitted

1 medium head Romaine lettuce

2 Tbsp. White wine vinegar

½ cup Honey

1 Tbsp. Fresh basil

1/4 cup Vegetable oil

½ cup Croutons

Preparation:

In a small bowl, combine the white wine vinegar, honey, and vegetable oil. Stir and pour onto the bowl containing lettuce. Throw in the apricots, basil and a handful of croutons. Serve and enjoy!

Amount Per Serving:

Serves: 2 • Serving size: 221 g

Calories 73

Total Fat 1.0g, Cholesterol 0mg

Sodium 62mg, potassium 343mg

Total carbohydrates 14.4g, sugars 4.8 g

Protein 2.1g

Vitamin A 15% • Vitamin C 2% • Calcium 2% • Iron 27%

17.   Orange chiffon cake

Orange increases the amount of citrate in the urine that appears to decrease calcium levels in the urine, reducing the amount of crystal formation or kidney stones.

Ingredients:

4 Eggs

½ cup Honey

3/4 cup flour

2 Tbsp. Orange juice

1/2 tsp. Orange extract

Preparation:

Preheat oven to 350F.

In a medium-sized bowl, beat the eggs and add the honey. Sift the flour into the egg and honey mixture and blend until consistency is smooth. Add the orange juice and orange extract. Pour batter into a greased loaf pan and bake for an hour. Turn loaf pan upside down until cake falls and slides down from the pan. Cool and serve.

18.   Sweetened grape salad

Grapes is rich in antioxidants which protect the body against oxidative stress and neutralizes oxidizing free radicals in the body. It is effective in cleansing the liver and kidneys by flushing out the uric acid in the urine.

Ingredients:

1 cup Red grapes, seedless

1 cup Green grapes, seedless

1 cup Sour cream

1 cup Cream cheese

½ cup Condensed milk

½ cup Honey

1 tsp. Vanilla extract

Preparation:

In a medium-sized bowl, throw in all ingredients and mix. Serve chilled and enjoy!

Amount Per Serving:

 Serves: 4 • Serving size: 201 g

Calories 482

Total Fat 35.8g, Cholesterol 102mg

Sodium 252mg, potassium 383mg

Total carbohydrates 32.8g, sugars 28.6g

Protein 9.5g

Vitamin A 26% • Vitamin C 6% • Calcium 23% • Iron 5%

19. Watermelon soup

Watermelon is a diuretic that is 95% water weight. It is helpful in flushing out very small kidney stones. It is also a rich source of potassium, which is a mineral that has an ability to dissolve kidney stones allowing the residue to pass. Watermelons is also high in lycopene and nitric oxide which are important elements in maintaining kidney health. Its black seeds are useful in cleansing the kidneys which help remove stones.

Ingredients:

6 cups Watermelon, peeled and cubed

3 oz. Lime juice

3 Tbsp. Honey

1 Tbsp. Fresh mint

3 oz. White wine

2 Tbsp. Ginger, minced

1 tsp. Cilantro

Preparation:

Combine all and process until mixture is smooth. Cover and chill for 4 hours. Serve in chilled bowls.

Amount Per Serving:

Serves: 4 • Serving size: 290g

Calories 149

Total Fat 0.5g, Cholesterol 0mg

Sodium 6mg, potassium 351mg

Total carbohydrates 34.5g, sugars 27.6g

Protein 1.8g

Vitamin A 28% • Vitamin C 42% • Calcium 3% • Iron7 %

20.   Apple cake

Apple contains citrate, a compound that inhibits the development of carbonate stones and calcium oxalate. It is a good source of fiber and vitamin C which is essential for fighting off infections.

Ingredients:

1 1/2 cup Flour

1/2 cup Honey

½ tsp. baking soda

¼ tsp. Cinnamon

3 Eggs, beaten

½ cup Vegetable oil

1 tsp. Vanilla extract

2 cups Apples, minced

1/4 cup apple juice

Preparation:

Preheat oven to 350F.

To make cake, combine, flour, honey, eggs, apple juice, oil and cinnamon in large bowl. Add the apple and mix well.

Pour into a greased pan 9x13 pan and bake for 45 minutes. Cool in pan for 25 minutes.

Spread batter in a greased and floured 9 x 13-inch pan. Bake at 350°F for 45-50 minutes.

Amount per Serving:

Serves: 5 • Serving size: 143 g

Calories 398

Total Fat 24.9g, Cholesterol 98mg

Sodium 164mg, potassium m139g

Total carbohydrates 36.5g, sugars 6.3g

Protein 7.3g

Vitamin A 3% • Vitamin C 14% • Calcium 2% • Iron 14%

21. Honeydew melon lime shake

Limes are high in Vitamin C which fights off infection and boosts immune system. It is high in anti-oxidant and have anti-biotic and anti-cancer properties. It contains flavonoids that effectively stops cancer cell division.

Ingredients:

5 Ice cubes

½ Lime, peeled

2 Tbsp. Honey

2 cups Honey lemon, cubed

1 Mint leaf

Preparation:

Blend all ingredients in a blender, transfer to a chilled glass and top with mint leaf.

Amount Per Serving:

Serves: 1 • Serving size: 354 g

Calories 234

Total Fat 0.6g, Cholesterol 0mg

Sodium 52mg, potassium 855mg

Total carbohydrates 60.1g, sugars 59.0g

Protein2.8 g

Vitamin A 211% • Vitamin C 191% • Calcium 3% • Iron 5%

22.   Garden salad with grapefruit avocado dressing

Avocados are an excellent source of potassium that help decrease urinary calcium excretion and lowers the risk of kidney stone formation.

Ingredients:

4 cups Loosely packed mixed greens

1 cup Grapefruit

1 Avocado, peeled, pitted and sliced

½ cup Olive oil

Preparation:

In a food processor, combine the grapefruit, avocado, and olive oil. Blend well and set aside.

Arrange mixed greens in a bowl and top with the grapefruit avocado dressing.

Amount Per Serving:

Serves: 5 • Serving size: 253 g

Calories 364

Total Fat 28.3g, Cholesterol 0mg

Sodium 53mg, potassium 505mg

Total carbohydrates 26.2g, sugars 8.0 g

Protein 5.2g

Vitamin A 134% • Vitamin C 41% • Calcium 5% • Iron 8%

23.   Cabbage omelet

Cabbage contains high amount of vitamin C which enhances the body's resistance to infection and inflammation. It is able to help prevent constipation which is a common complication among kidney disease patients. It is low in sodium which prevents water retention and facilitates passing out of kidney stones through urine excretion.

Ingredients:

¼ cup Cabbage

¼ cup Cheddar cheese, shredded

1 Tbsp. Milk

1 Tbsp. Onion

2 Eggs

1 Tbsp. Olive oil for cooking

Preparation:

Whip egg until smooth, slowly pour in the milk and whip again. Throw in all remaining ingredients.

In a non-stick skillet, over medium-heat, heat the oil and slowly pour the egg mixture, spread evenly. Cook until the egg is firm and no longer runny, or for about 1-2 minutes. Gently fold the omelet in half. Serve on plate.

Amount Per Serving:

Serves: 1 • Serving size: 174 g

Calories 376

Total Fat 32.5g, Cholesterol 358mg

Sodium 309mg, potassium 199mg

Total carbohydrates 3.7g, sugars 2.5g

Protein 18.9g

Vitamin A 15% • Vitamin C 12% • Calcium 28% • Iron 11%

24.   Stir fried cauliflower

Cauliflower is a good source of vitamins C and K which help promote strong bones and keep the skeletal structure healthy. It has an anti-inflammatory, antioxidant, anti-clotting and calcification properties. It also has a detoxification property that helps support proper nutrient absorption and waste removal of toxins from the body.

Ingredients:

2 cups Cauliflower

150 g. Ground chicken

1 Tbsp. Onion

1 Tbsp. Carrot

½ tsp. Cardamom

1/8 tsp. Pepper

1 Tbsp. Olive oil

Preparation:

Over medium heat, heat the olive oil and sauté the onion until translucent and the garlic until light brown. Add the ground chicken, stir and cook until evenly light brown. Add the carrot and cook until tender. Add the cauliflower and cardamom. Turn off heat and gently stir-fry the cauliflower in very low heat to preserve nutrients.

Amount Per Serving:

 Serves: 1 • Serving size: 368 g

Calories 275

Total Fat 5.6g, Cholesterol 110mg

Sodium 151mg, potassium 1289mg

Total carbohydrates 13.1g, sugars5.6 g

Protein 50.5g

Vitamin A 24% • Vitamin C 157% • Calcium 6% • Iron 16%

25.   Onion soup with parsley sprigs

Onion is a potent and effective home remedy/medicinal food used in dissolving kidney stones. It has antiseptic, diuretic and anti-inflammatory properties. It also cleanses the body from toxicity and aids in urinary infections.

Ingredients:

1 Onion, whole

1 cup Chicken, shredded

1 Tbsp. Parsley sprigs

1 cup Green onion, chopped

1/8 tsp. Pepper

1 Egg

Preparation:

Boil whole onion in one liter of water. Add chicken and simmer for 5-7 minutes until chicken is completely cooked. Add green onion, parsley, pepper and egg. Stir lightly and remove from fire.

Amount Per Serving:

 Serves: 1 • Serving size: 398 g

Calories 352

Total Fat 9.0g, Cholesterol 271mg

Sodium 172mg, potassium 782mg

Total carbohydrates 18.4g, sugars 7.4g

Protein 49.3g

Vitamin A 31% • Vitamin C 53% • Calcium 15% • Iron 23%

26.   Chicken quesadilla with garlic aioli

Garlic is considered to be a natural antibiotic used for treating a wide variety of infections. It helps eliminate toxins and the body, improves blood circulation and cleanses the blood which is important for kidney disease patients.

Ingredients:

3 medium Garlic

1 Tbsp. Extra virgin olive oil

1/8 tsp. Basil

1 cup Mayonnaise

¼ cup Lemon juice

2 Tbsp. Mozzarella cheese, grated

½ Tbsp. Mustard

1/8 tsp. Cayenne pepper

1/8 tsp. Parsley

1 Tbsp. Olive oil

2 Wheat tortillas

Preparation:

Preheat the oven to 425 degrees F.

To roast the garlic, get a whole garlic and cut off the top end to expose the garlic cloves. Wrap in an aluminum foil drizzled with olive oil and sprinkled with basil and pepper. Bake for 35 to 45 minutes. Remove from foil and cool. Squeeze the pulp to remove from skins.

In a food processor, combine the roasted garlic, lemon juice, mayonnaise, mustard, pepper, and cayenne. Blend in a food processor until well combined. Refrigerate. Garnish with parsley.

Layer one tortilla with mozzarella cheese followed by a spread of garlic aioli. Cover with the other tortilla. Microwave for one minute. Enjoy hot!

Amount Per Serving:

Serves: 3 • Serving size: 172 g

Calories 413

Total Fat 34.9g, Cholesterol 30mg

Sodium 674mg, potassium 47mg

Total carbohydrates 20.5g, sugars 5.6 g

Protein 6.7g

Vitamin A4 % • Vitamin C 16% • Calcium 4% • Iron 2%

27.   Chicken with cherry salad

Cherries are rich in potassium, antioxidants and anthocyanins, chemicals that prevent uric acid into forming into crystals. The potassium in the cherry makes the urine more alkaline.

Ingredients:

1 medium Romaine lettuce

1 cup Leftover chicken, shredded

¾ cup Cherries

½ cup Mustard

1 cup Mayonnaise

1 Tbsp. Honey

Preparation:

To make the dressing, in a medium-sized bowl, combine the mustard, mayonnaise and honey.

In a separate bowl, combine the lettuce, chicken and cherries together. Pour dressing on top and serve.

Amount Per Serving:

Serves: 3 • Serving size: 266 g

Calories 536

Total Fat 35.4g, Cholesterol 56mg

Sodium 594mg, potassium 430mg

Total carbohydrates 37.0g, sugars 13.6g

Protein 21.3g

Vitamin A 4% • Vitamin C 16% • Calcium 16% • Iron 34%

28. Orange cranberry cake

Cranberry is known to prevent urinary tract infection, and therefore is helpful in preventing the formation of struvite stones. This type of stone is made of ammonium, phosphate and magnesium which only occurs in the presence of urinary tract infection. Cranberry juice contains polyphenols which has antibacterial and antiviral properties. It also has an anti-oxidant property that protects against aging. Since it contains high levels of acidity, it blocks the bacteria from attaching to the renal walls. Cranberry is also rich in vitamin C which strengthens the immune system.

Ingredients:

1 cup Cranberries

1 Tbsp. grated orange zest

¼ cup Orange juice

2 cups Flour

1 ½ cup Olive oil

½ cup Honey

4 Eggs

2 Tbsp. water

1 tsp. Vanilla extract

1 tsp. Cinnamon

Preparation:

Preheat the oven to 350F.

In a mixing bowl, combine cranberries, orange juice, orange zest, cinnamon, vanilla extract, honey and olive oil and whisk using a hand-processed blender until smooth and creamy. Add the flour and one egg then blend. Keep adding flour and one egg at a time until consistency of mixture is smooth. Pour batter in a greased rectangular bread tin. Bake in the oven for 50-60 minutes

Amount Per Serving:

Serves: 12 • Serving size: 85 g

Calories 333

Total Fat 27.4g, Cholesterol 123mg

Sodium 204mg, potassium 78mg

Total carbohydrates 17.7g, sugars 1.0g

Protein 4.3g

Vitamin A 18% • Vitamin C 12% • Calcium 2% • Iron 8%

29.   Coconut pineapple smoothie

Coconut contains high amount of potassium which helps in dissolving kidney stones. It also plays a key role in alkalizing the urine thereby preventing the formation of kidney stones.

Ingredients:

1 cups Coconut water

1 cup Pineapple, chopped

3 cups Coconut meat, shredded

6 ice cubes

Preparation:

Throw in all ingredients in a blender, shake and enjoy!

Amount Per Serving:

 Serves: 6 • Serving size: 108 g

Calories 247

Total Fat 22.9 g, Cholesterol 0mg

Sodium 14mg, potassium 278mg

Total carbohydrates 11.9g, sugars 6.5g

Protein 2.4g

Vitamin A 0% • Vitamin C 28% • Calcium 1% • Iron 35%

30.   Pearl Barley Risotto

Barley prevents the kidney stone formation. It cleanses the kidney by flushing toxic wastes out of the body through the urine. Barley is rich in dietary fiber required for reducing the excretion of calcium in the urine.

Ingredients:

1 ½ cup Barley, soaked overnight (1:2 barley: water ratio)

1 Tbsp. Garlic

3 cups Chicken stock

2 Tbsp. Onion

2 tsp. Olive oil

2 Tbsp. Parmesan cheese, shredded

½ cup Leftover chicken, shredded

½ cup Carrots, minced

½ cup corn

Preparation:

Over medium heat, sauté onion until translucent in olive oil. Throw in the leftover chicken, carrots, corn and pour the chicken stock. Heat it up with the bay leaf until simmering. Add the garlic then add the barley. Lower the heat and simmer for 45-50 minutes or until barley is completely cooked. Top with parmesan cheese, garnish with parsley, transfer to a plate and serve hot.

Amount Per Serving:

Serves: 5 • Serving size: 236 g

Calories 236

Total Fat 3.2g, Cholesterol 4mg

Sodium 484mg, potassium 342mg

Total carbohydrates 46.0g, sugars 2.1g

Protein 8.0g

Vitamin A 38% • Vitamin C 4% • Calcium 4% • Iron 14%

31.   Creamy red beans soup

Kidney beans are an excellent source folate, dietary fiber, copper and molybdenum. Kidney beans are a good source of manganese, phosphorus, protein, vitamin B1, iron, and potassium. It normalizes urination and increases the quantity of urine. It aids in treatment of urinary tract infection.

Ingredients:

1 tablespoon olive oil

2 Tbsp. Garlic, minced

2 Tbsp. Onion, diced

2 (1-pound) cans Red kidney beans

1 tsp. Garlic powder

¼ tsp. Ground black pepper

½ cup Green bell pepper, minced

2 1/2 cups Chicken stock

1 Tbsp. Cilantro

Preparation:

Heat olive oil over medium-high heat in a large saucepan, sauté garlic and onion until tender. Stir in kidney beans, garlic powder, bell pepper and pepper. Pour in chicken stock. Lower heat and simmer for 1 ½ to 2 hours or until kidney beans are tender and the consistency is smooth and creamy.

Amount Per Serving:

Serves: 8 • Serving size: 202 g

Calories 408

Total Fat 3.2g, Cholesterol 0mg

Sodium 253mg, potassium 1575mg

Total carbohydrates 71.3g, sugars 3.1g

Protein 26.1g

Vitamin A 4% • Vitamin C 22% • Calcium 10% • Iron 43 %

32.   Uva ursi smoothie

Uva ursi is commonly referred to as bearberry, because bears enjoy eating the plant's fruit. It is widely used for treating kidney stones and other bladder conditions. It contains a natural compound, arbutin, which has a diuretic effect that help encourage the urge to urinate. As it passes through the kidney, it cleanses the harmful organisms. Its astringent property reduces irritation and encourages excretion of toxic wastes. Its anti-lithic property prevents the kidney from building crystals.

Ingredients:

½ tsp. Uva ursi leaves

1 Banana

½ cup Honey

1 tsp. Vanilla extract

1 cup Plain yogurt

Preparation:

Simmer uva ursi leaves in 1 cup of water for 20 minutes. Cool.

Transfer to a blender and add other ingredients. Shake well, serve chilled.

Amount Per Serving:

Serves: 2 • Serving size: 182 g

Calories 140

Total Fat 1.7g, Cholesterol 7mg

Sodium 86mg, potassium 498mg

Total carbohydrates 22.1g, sugars 15.8g

Protein7.6 g

Vitamin A 2% • Vitamin C 10% • Calcium 23 % • Iron 1%

33.   Red and green grapes

Grapes contain high amounts of vitamin B6, K, C, thiamine and resveratrol, which has anti-aging, anti-cancer anti-viral and anti-inflammation properties. It also contains anthocyanin which lowers the risk of heart disease.

Ingredients:

¾ cup Red and green grapes

1/3 cup White wine vinegar

1 Tbsp. Fresh oregano

1 tsp. Garlic, crushed

1 cup Olive oil

Preparation:

Combine all ingredients together until smooth. Chill inside the refrigerator.

Pour dressing on top of mixed greens.

Amount Per Serving:

 Serves: 3 • Serving size: 124 g

Calories 603

Total Fat 67.4g, Cholesterol 0mg

Sodium 2mg, potassium 92mg

Total carbohydrates 5.5g, sugars 3.9g

Protein0.4 g

Vitamin A 3% • Vitamin C 3% • Calcium 3% • Iron 5%

34.   Cold plum soup

Plumes contain high amounts of vitamin C and phytonutrients that are known to fight diabetes, arthritis, cognitive and heart diseases. It is an effective laxative because of its sorbitol, isatin and fiber contents.

Ingredients:

10 Plums, halved and pitted

½ cup Water

½ cup Honey

1 scoop Lemon basil gelato

Preparation:

In a pot, over low heat, cook the plums in water and add honey. Cook until tender and juices are released. Remove from heat. Sift plums, cool and serve chilled with lemon basil gelato.

Amount Per Serving:

 Serves: 3 • Serving size: 261 g

Calories 71

Total Fat 0.4g, Cholesterol 0mg

Sodium 1mg, potassium 229mg

Total carbohydrates17.9 g, sugars 15.7g

Protein 1.0g

Vitamin A 11% • Vitamin C 22% • Calcium 0% • Iron 2%

35.   Parsley pesto pasta

Parsley is known for its kidney-cleansing properties because of its two potent ingredients, myristicin and apiol, which are found to have diuretic properties.

Ingredients:

1 cup Fresh parsley leaves

2 Tbsp. Garlic, chopped finely

½ tsp. Garlic powder

1 cup Parmesan cheese, grated

3/4 cup Olive oil

100 g. Pasta

Preparation:

Cook pasta according to package instruction.

In a food processor, throw in all ingredients and blend well until consistency is smooth. Serve with pasta and enjoy!

Amount Per Serving:

 Serves: 2 • Serving size: 170 g

Calories 818

Total Fat 77.0 g, Cholesterol 37mg

Sodium m31g, potassium 297mg

Total carbohydrates32.6 g, sugars 0.5g

Protein7.2 g

Vitamin A 51% • Vitamin C 71% • Calcium 6% • Iron 21%

36.   Crispy fried plantain

Plantain is considered as one of the best kidney stone natural remedy. The leaves of plantain is proven to be effective in dissolving kidney stones. The stem of plantain is believed to be effective in eliminating kidney stones that have formed in the urinary tract. This is the reason why traditional medicine uses this for treating bloody and cloudy urine, prostitis and kidney stones.

Ingredients:

3 cups Ripe plantains, thinly sliced into 3"

3 Tbsp. Flour

1/4 cup Olive oil

Preparation:

In a frying pan, over medium heat, heat the olive oil and fry the flour dredged in flour. Fry until plantain is golden brown.

Remove excess oil by placing on a plate lined with napkin before transferring to a serving plate. Enjoy while hot and crispy.

Amount Per Serving:

Serves: 2 • Serving size: 261 g

Calories 530

Total Fat 26.1g, Cholesterol 0mg

Sodium 9mg, potassium 1120mg

Total carbohydrates 79.7g, sugars 33.3 g

Protein 4.1g

Vitamin A 50% • Vitamin C 68% • Calcium 1% • Iron 10 %

37.   Rosemary chicken sandwich

Rosemary, when consumed regularly, increases the flow of urine thereby reducing one's susceptibility from producing kidney stones. It primarily works by inhibiting the activities of urea, which contributes in the stone formation.

Ingredients:

1/2 cup Leftover chicken, shredded

1 Tbsp. Onions, chopped

1 Tbsp. Plain low-fat yogurt

1 Tbsp. Mayonnaise

1/2 tsp. Rosemary

1/2 tsp. Dijon mustard

1/8 teaspoon salt

1/8 tsp. Black pepper

2 slices Wheat bread

Preparation:

In a small bowl, combine all ingredients. Mix well. Spread generously on top of a slice of wheat bread. Cover with another slice of bread and enjoy!

Amount Per Serving:

Serves: 1 • Serving size: 170 g

Calories 321

Total Fat 9.3g, Cholesterol 59mg

Sodium 744mg, potassium 334mg

Total carbohydrates 29.3 g, sugars 5.6g

Protein 28.8g

Vitamin A 2% • Vitamin C 2% • Calcium11 % • Iron 13%

38.   Watermelon and feta salad

Regular consumption of watermelon cleanses the kidneys. It's diuretic property increases urine volume resulting to kidney stone prevention. This fruit is also rich in potassium which is beneficial in dissolving kidney stones, eases the pain associated with passing of the stone and helps the body in eliminating them.

Ingredients:

2 cups Watermelon, diced

3 cups Loosely packed mixed greens

3/4 cup Arugula

3/4 cup Feta cheese, cubed

3 Tbsp. Balsamic vinegar

1/4 cup Olive oil

Preparation:

Throw in all ingredients in a salad bowl. Mix, serve and enjoy!

Amount Per Serving:

Serves: 3 • Serving size: 359 g

Calories 396

Total Fat 25.2g, Cholesterol 33mg

Sodium 486mg, potassium 473mg

Total carbohydrates 33.3g, sugars 13.6g

Protein 11.3 g

Vitamin A 173% • Vitamin C 25% • Calcium 25% • Iron 12%

39.   Sweetened creamy banana

Bananas are very rich in magnesium and potassium which help in preventing kidney stone formation. The magnesium combines readily with oxalates present in foods inhibiting the growth of a certain type of kidney stone, calcium oxalates crystals. On the other hand, potassium balances the acidity of urine thereby preventing formation of calcium oxalates crystals.

Ingredients:

6 ripe Plantain bananas, halved in lengthwise

¼ cup Honey

1/4 cup Sweetened condensed milk

1/8 tsp. Cinnamon powder

1 cup Vegetable oil

Preparation:

In a skillet over low heat, fry the bananas in vegetable oil. Once it is golden brown pour honey on top of the bananas until completely covered. Once it is dark brown, remove from fire, transfer to a serving plate and pour sweetened condensed milk on top. Sprinkle with cinnamon.

Amount Per Serving:

Serves: 5 • Serving size: 247 g

Calories 363

Total Fat 2.1g, Cholesterol 5mg

Sodium 29mg, potassium 1138mg

Total carbohydrates 90.8g, sugars 54.5g

Protein4.0 g

Vitamin A 49% • Vitamin C 67% • Calcium 5% • Iron8 %

40.   Vegetarian pizza

Asparagus increases urine production and is used in preventing stones in the kidney and bladder. It contains high amounts of vitamins C, E, B6, dietary fiber and folic acid.

Ingredients:

1 cup Asparagus, sliced into 2"

1/2 cup Bell pepper

½ cup Dijon mustard

Pizza dough:

1 cup Flour

1 Tbsp. yeast

2 Tbsp. Honey

2 Tbsp. Olive oil

½ cup Warm water

Caramelized onions:

5 Tbsp. Olive oil

2 1/2 lbs. White onions, thinly sliced

2 Tbsp. Honey

Preparation:

Caramelize the onions by sautéing onion in olive oil. Cook until onion is soft or for about 20 minutes. Add the honey and stir. Scrape the browned bits from the pan to avoid the burned taste. Remove from heat.

Preheat the oven in 500C.

To make the pizza dough, combine half of the flour, yeast and honey. Add warm water and olive oil. Combine until consistency is smooth. Start kneading the dough on a floured surface, gradually adding the flour until the dough is no longer sticking to your hands. Knead until dough is smooth and elastic. Grease a mixing bowl. Place the dough in the bowl. Set aside in a warm place to let it rise for 25 minutes. After rising, place the dough on a cookie sheet lined with a parchment paper. Spread the dough in to a circle.

Spread the Dijon mustard on the unbaked crust. Layer with caramelized onions. Top with bell pepper and asparagus. Bake for 15 minutes and enjoy.

Amount per Serving:

Serves: 5 • Serving size: 368 g

Calories 396

Total Fat19.8 g, Cholesterol 18mg

Sodium 346mg, potassium 521mg

Total carbohydrates 51.0 g, sugar17.7s g

Protein 7.9g

Vitamin A 15% • Vitamin C 49% • Calcium 8% • Iron17 %

41. Fruit salad with ginger yogurt

Ginger has an anti-inflammatory, anti-bacterial, anti-viral, and anti-parasitic properties. It prevents kidney stones by dissolving it. It is also a natural diuretic that helps in flushing out kidney stones and other toxic wastes from the body.

Ingredients:

1 cup Pineapple, sliced

3 navel oranges, peeled and cubed

1/2 cup Dried cranberries

2 Tbsp. honey

1/4 tsp. Cinnamon

16 oz. Greek yogurt

2/3 cup Crystallized ginger, mixed

¾ cup Honey

½ cup Graham cracker crumbs

Preparation:

Combine pineapple, oranges, dried cranberries, honey and cinnamon. Cover with a cling wrap and refrigerate for an hour. Mix yogurt and ginger in a bowl. Sprinkle graham cracker crumbs. Enjoy!

Amount Per Serving:

Serves: 5 • Serving size: 276 g

Calories 214

Total Fat 2.9g, Cholesterol 5mg

Sodium 106mg, potassium 421mg

Total carbohydrates 37.4g, sugars 26.4g

Protein 11.1g

Vitamin A 6% • Vitamin C 130 % • Calcium 15% • Iron 5%

42. Creamy chicken macaroni soup

Celery is an effective diuretic that helps flush out toxins and wastes deposited in the kidney and urinary tract. This attribute makes the celery effective in passing kidney stones. It is also rich in vitamin C, which acts as an antioxidant.

Ingredients:

1 cup Leftover chicken, shredded

200g. Uncooked elbow macaroni

1 can Evaporated milk

½ cup Carrots, diced

½ cup Celery, diced

5 cups Chicken broth

1 Tbsp. Onion

1 Tbsp. Olive oil

Preparation:

Over medium heat, sauté onion in olive oil until translucent. Add the chicken, chicken broth, evaporated milk and the macaroni pasta. Simmer in low heat for 10 minutes. Throw in the vegetables and heat for 2 minutes or until vegetables are tender. Remove from heat and serve hot.

Amount Per Serving:

Serves: 7 • serving size: 291 g

Calories 256

Total Fat 8.0g, Cholesterol 31mg

Sodium 627mg, potassium 454mg

Total carbohydrates 28.4g, sugars 7.1g

Protein 16.7g

Vitamin A 29% • Vitamin C 3% • Calcium 16% • Iron 9%

JUICES

1.   Carrot Spinach Juice

Ingredients:

3 large carrots

1 bunch of spinach, torn

1 cup of cauliflower, chopped

1 cup of Swiss chards, torn

¼ tsp of Himalayan salt

2 oz. of water

Preparation:

Wash the carrots and chop into thick slices. Set aside.

Combine spinach and Swiss chards in a colander and wash thoroughly under cold running water. Drain, and torn with hands. Set aside.

Trim off the outer leaves of a cauliflower. Wash it and cut into small pieces. Reserve the rest in the refrigerator.

Now, combine carrots, spinach, Swiss chards, and cauliflower in a juicer and process until juiced.

Transfer to serving glasses and stir in the salt and water.

Add few ice cubes and serve immediately.

Nutritional information per serving: Kcal: 138, Protein: 14.4g, Carbs: 39.7g, Fats: 2.2g

2.   Avocado Broccoli Juice

Ingredients:

1 cup of avocado, chopped

1 cup of broccoli, chopped

1 large cucumber

1 large lemon, peeled

1 large lime, peeled

3 oz. of water

Preparation:

Peel the avocado and cut in half. Remove the pit and cut into chunks. Set aside.

Wash the broccoli and chop into small pieces. Set aside.

Wash the cucumber and cut in thick slices. Set aside.

Peel the lemon and lime. Cut lengthwise in half. Set aside.

Now, process avocado, broccoli, cucumber, lemon, and lime in a juicer. Transfer to serving glasses and stir in the water.

Add some ice and serve immediately.

Note:

Lemon and lime contain a high amount of citrate, so make sure to add more water than usual.

Nutritional information per serving: Kcal: 281, Protein: 8.3g, Carbs: 38.8g, Fats: 22.8g

3.   Blueberries Watermelon Juice

Ingredients:

2 cups of blueberries

2 cups of watermelon, seeded

1 large grapefruit, chopped

1 tbsp. of liquid honey

2 oz. of water

Preparation:

Wash the blueberries under cold running water. Drain and set aside.

Cut the watermelon lengthwise. For 2 cups, you will need about 2 large wedges. Peel and cut into chunks. Remove the seeds and set aside. Reserve the rest of the melon for some other juices.

Peel the grapefruit and divide into wedges. Set aside.

Now, process blueberries, watermelon, and grapefruit in a juicer. Transfer to serving glasses and stir in the honey and water.

Refrigerate for 15 minutes before serving.

Enjoy!

Nutritional information per serving: Kcal: 375, Protein: 5.9g, Carbs: 92.1g, Fats: 1.7g

4.   Coconut Mango Juice

Ingredients:

1 large mango, chopped

1 cup of pomegranate seeds

1 large carrot

1 small Granny Smith apple, cored

2 oz. of coconut water

Preparation:

Wash the mango and cut into small chunks. Set aside.

Cut the top of the pomegranate fruit using a sharp knife. Slice down to each of the white membranes inside of the fruit. Pop the seeds into a medium bowl.

Wash the carrot and cut into thick slices. Set aside.

Wash the apple and remove the core. Cut into bite-sized pieces and set aside.

Now, combine mango, pomegranate seeds, carrot, and apple in a juicer and process until juiced.

Transfer to serving glasses and stir in the coconut water.

Refrigerate or add some ice and serve immediately.

Nutritional information per serving: Kcal: 338, Protein: 5.5g, Carbs: 94.1g, Fats: 2.7g

5. Cherry Tomato-Watercress Juice

Ingredients:

1 cup of cherry tomatoes, halved

1 cup of watercress, chopped

1 cup of pumpkin, chopped

1 cup of collard greens, chopped

1 large cucumber

Preparation:

Wash the tomatoes and place them in a bowl. Cut in half and reserve the juice in the bowl while cutting. Set aside.

Combine watercress and collard greens in a colander and wash thoroughly. Torn with hands and set aside.

Peel the pumpkin and cut in half. Scoop out the seeds using a spoon. Cut one large wedge and peel it. Cut into small chunks and set aside. Reserve the rest for later.

Wash the cucumber and cut into thick slices. Set aside.

Now, process tomatoes, watercress, collard greens, pumpkin, and cucumber in a juicer. Transfer to serving glasses and stir in the reserved tomato juice. Add some ice before serving.

Nutritional information per serving: Kcal: 96, Protein: 6.4g, Carbs: 27.4g, Fats: 1g

6. Spinach Artichoke Juice

Ingredients:

1 large bunch of spinach

1 large artichoke head

1 cup of sweet potatoes, cubed

1 cup of turnip greens, chopped

1 cup of basil, chopped

2 oz. of water

¼ tsp of Himalayan salt

Preparation:

Combine spinach, turnip greens, and basil in a colander and wash under cold running water. Drain and chop it roughly with your hands and set aside.

Trim off the outer leaves of the artichoke using a sharp knife. Cut into bite-sized pieces and set aside.

Peel the sweet potato and cut into chunks. Set aside.

Now, process spinach, turnip greens, basil, artichoke, and sweet potato in a juicer. Transfer to serving glasses and stir in the water and Himalayan salt.

Add some ice and serve immediately.

Nutritional information per serving: Kcal: 202, Protein: 18.6g, Carbs: 60.7g, Fats: 1.9g

7.   Butternut Squash Bean Juice

Ingredients:

1 cup of butternut squash, chopped

1 cup of green beans, chopped

1 cup fresh celery, torn

1 cup of purple cabbage, torn

1 large cucumber

1 large green bell pepper, seeded

¼ tsp of Himalayan salt

2 oz. of water

Preparation:

Peel the butternut squash and remove the seeds using a spoon. Cut into small cubes and reserve the rest of the squash for some other recipe. Wrap in a plastic foil and refrigerate.

Combine purple cabbage and celery in a colander and wash under cold running water. Drain and torn with hands. Set aside.

Wash the green beans cut into bite-sized pieces. Set aside.

Wash the cucumber and cut into thick slices. Set aside.

Wash the bell pepper and cut in half. Remove the seeds and chop into small pieces. Set aside.

Now, process butternut squash, cabbage, celery, green beans, cucumber, and bell pepper in a juicer.

Transfer to serving glasses and stir in the salt and water. Refrigerate for 30 minutes before serving.

Enjoy!

Nutritional information per serving: Kcal: 163, Protein: 7.7g, Carbs: 48.2g, Fats: 1.1g

8.   Kiwi Carrot Juice

Ingredients:

2 large kiwis, peeled

2 large carrots

1 large Honeycrisp apple, cored

1 cup of mint, chopped

1 large orange, peeled

2 oz. of water

Preparation:

Peel the kiwis and cut lengthwise in half. Set aside.

Wash the carrots and cut into thick slices. Set aside

Wash the apple and remove the core. Cut into bite-sized pieces and set aside.

Wash the fresh mint and roughly chop it. Set aside.

Now, combine kiwis, carrots, apple, and mint in a juicer and process until juiced. Transfer to serving glasses and add some ice before serving.

Enjoy!

Nutritional information per serving: Kcal: 292, Protein: 6.1g, Carbs: 88.6g, Fats: 1.8g

9.   Bloody Beets Juice

Ingredients:

2 large beets, trimmed

1 large red apple, cored

1 cup of pomegranate seeds

1 large cucumber

1 small ginger knob, 1-inch

Preparation:

Wash the beets and trim off the green parts. Cut into small pieces and set aside.

Wash the apple and remove the core. Cut into bite-sized pieces and set aside.

Cut the top of the pomegranate fruit using a sharp knife. Slice down to each of the white membranes inside of the fruit. Pop the seeds into a medium bowl.

Wash the cucumber and cut into thick slices. Set aside.

Peel the ginger knob and set aside.

Now, process beets, apple, pomegranate seeds, cucumber and ginger knob in a juicer. Transfer to serving glasses and add some ice. You can stir in one tablespoon of honey, but this is optional.

Serve immediately.

Nutritional information per serving: Kcal: 285, Protein: 8g, Carbs: 81.6g, Fats: 2.2g

10.   Carrot Grape Juice

Ingredients:

3 large carrots

1 cup of green grapes

1 Granny Smith apple, cored

1 large lemon, peeled

A handful of spinach

2 oz. of water

Preparation:

Wash the carrots and cut into thick slices. Set aside.

Wash the grapes and set aside.

Wash the apple and remove the core. Cut into bite-sized pieces and set aside.

Peel the lemon and cut lengthwise in half. Set aside.

Wash the spinach thoroughly under cold running water. Roughly chop it and set aside.

Now, combine carrots, grapes, apple, lemon, and spinach in a juicer and process until juiced. Transfer to serving glasses and stir in the water.

Refrigerate for 20 minutes before serving.

Nutritional information per serving: Kcal: 208, Protein: 1.4g, Carbs: 62.6g, Fats: 1.4g

11.   Green Crookneck Juice

Ingredients:

1 cup of crookneck squash

1 cup of collard greens, torn

1 cup of kale, torn

1 cup Romaine lettuce, torn

1 large cucumber

½ tsp of Himalayan salt

¼ tsp of Cayenne pepper, ground

2 oz. of water

Preparation:

Wash the crookneck squash and cut in half. Scoop out the seeds using a spoon. Cut into small chunks and set aside. Reserve the rest for another juice.

Combine collard greens, kale, and lettuce in a colander. Wash thoroughly under cold running water and torn with hands. Set aside.

Wash the cucumber and chop into thick slices. Set aside.

Now, combine crookneck squash, collard greens, kale, lettuce, and cucumber in a juicer and process until juiced.

Transfer to serving glasses and stir in the salt, Cayenne pepper, and water. Refrigerate for 15 minutes before serving.

Nutritional information per serving: Kcal: 91, Protein: 7.8g, Carbs: 25.2g, Fats: 1.6g

12. Honeydew Cherry Juice

Ingredients:

1 large honeydew melon wedge

1 cup of fresh cherries

1 large lime, peeled

1 large orange, peeled

1 tbsp. of honey, raw

2 oz. of coconut water

Preparation:

Cut the honeydew melon lengthwise in half. Scoop out the seeds using a spoon. Cut the large wedges and peel them. Cut into small chunks and place in a bowl. Wrap the rest of the melon in a plastic foil and refrigerate.

Wash the cherries and cut in half. Remove the pits and set aside.

Peel the lime and cut lengthwise in half. Set aside.

Peel the orange and divide into wedges. Set aside.

Now, process honeydew melon, cherries, lime, and orange in a juicer. Transfer to serving glasses and stir in the honey and coconut water.

Add some ice and serve immediately.

Nutritional information per serving: Kcal: 276, Protein: 4.2g, Carbs: 78.9g, Fats: 0.7g

13.   Brussels Sprout Fennel Juice

Ingredients:

2 cups of Brussels sprouts

2 cups of fennel

1 cup of purple cabbage, torn

1 large lemon, peeled

1 cup of beet greens, torn

1 large cucumber

Preparation:

Wash the Brussels sprouts and trim off the outer leaves. Cut in half and set aside.

Wash the fennel bulb and trim off the wilted outer layers. Cut into small chunks and set aside.

Combine cabbage and beet greens in a colander and wash under cold running water. Torn with hands and set aside.

Wash the cucumber and cut into thick slices. Set aside.

Now, combine Brussels sprouts, fennel, cabbage, beet greens, and cucumber in a juicer and process until juiced.

Transfer to serving glasses and add few ice cubes before serving.

Nutritional information per serving: Kcal: 154, Protein: 12.8g, Carbs: 53g, Fats: 1.5g

14.   Orange Mango Juice

Ingredients:

1 cup of mango chunks

1 large orange, peeled

1 large green apple, cored

1 large lime, peeled

1 small ginger root knob, 1-inch

2 oz. of water

Preparation:

Wash the mango and cut into chunks. Fill the measuring cup and refrigerate the rest for some other juice.

Peel the orange and divide into wedges. Set aside.

Wash the apple and remove the core. Cut into bite-sized pieces and set aside.

Peel the lime and cut lengthwise in half. Set aside.

Peel the ginger knob and set aside.

Now, process mango, orange, apple, lime, and ginger in a juicer. Transfer to serving glasses and stir in the water.

Add some ice and serve immediately.

Nutritional information per serving: Kcal: 268, Protein: 12.8g, Carbs: 53g, Fats: 1.5g

15. Zucchini Pepper Juice

Ingredients:

2 large yellow bell peppers, chopped

1 large zucchini, chopped

1cup of watercress, torn

1 large carrot

1 cup of parsnips, chopped

½ tsp of Himalayan salt

Preparation:

Wash the bell peppers and cut in half. Remove the seeds and chop into small pieces. Set aside.

Peel the zucchini and cut in half. Scoop out the seeds and cut into small chunks. Set aside.

Wash the watercress thoroughly under cold running water and torn with hands. Set aside.

Wash the carrot and parsnips. Cut into bite-sized pieces and set aside.

Now, process bell peppers, zucchini, watercress, carrot, and parsnips in a juicer. Transfer to serving glasses and stir in the salt.

Refrigerate for 15 minutes before serving.

Nutritional information per serving: Kcal: 243, Protein: 11.2g, Carbs: 70g, Fats: 2.5g

16.   Asparagus Celery Juice

Ingredients:

1 cup of asparagus, trimmed

1 cup of celery, chopped

1 cup of fresh kale, torn

1 cup of mustard greens, torn

1 large lemon

1 large cucumber

Preparation:

Wash the asparagus and trim off the woody ends. Cut into small pieces and set aside.

Wash the celery thoroughly and cut into bite-sized pieces. Set aside.

Combine kale and mustard greens in a colander and wash under cold running water. Torn with hands and set aside.

Peel the lemon and cut lengthwise in half. Set aside.

Wash the cucumber and cut into thick slices. Set aside.

Now, process asparagus, celery, kale, mustard greens, lemon, and cucumber in a juicer.

Transfer to serving glasses and add few ice cubes before serving.

Nutritional information per serving: Kcal: 107, Protein: 10.7g, Carbs: 33g, Fats: 1.7g

17.   Raspberry Mint Juice

Ingredients:

2 cups of fresh raspberries

2 cups of fresh mint, torn

1 large orange

1 large green apple, cored

1 large lime

2 oz. of water

Preparation:

Wash the raspberries under cold running water and set aside.

Wash the mint thoroughly and torn with hands. Set aside.

Peel the orange and divide into wedges. Set aside.

Peel the apple and remove the core. Cut into bite-sized pieces and set aside.

Peel the lime and cut lengthwise in half. Set aside.

Now, process raspberries, mint, orange, apple, and lime in a juicer. Transfer to serving glasses and stir in the water.

Add some ice and serve immediately.

Nutritional information per serving: Kcal: 258, Protein: 7.6g, Carbs: 90.1g, Fats: 2.7g

18.   Tomato Pumpkin Juice

Ingredients:

1 cup of pumpkin, cubed

2 medium-sized Roma tomatoes, chopped

1 cup of fresh basil, torn

1 large cucumber

¼ tsp of dried oregano

½ tsp of sea salt

2 oz. of water

Preparation:

Peel the pumpkin and cut in half. Scoop out the seeds using a spoon. Cut one large wedge and peel it. Cut into small chunks and set aside. Reserve the rest for later.

Wash the tomatoes and place them in a bowl. Cut into quarters and reserve the juice while cutting. Set aside.

Wash the basil thoroughly under cold running water. Torn with hands and set aside.

Wash the cucumber and cut into thick slices. Set aside.

Now, process pumpkin, tomatoes, basil, and cucumber in a juicer. Transfer to serving glasses and stir in the oregano, salt, water, and reserved tomato juice.

Refrigerate for 10 minutes before serving.

Enjoy!

Nutritional information per serving: Kcal: 87, Protein: 4.9g, Carbs: 23.9g, Fats: 0.9g

19.   Blackberry Peach Juice

Ingredients:

1 cup of fresh blackberries

2 medium-sized peaches

1 large lemon

1 cup of cantaloupe, cubed

1 large carrot

1 small yellow apple, cored

2 oz. of water

Preparation:

Wash the blackberries under cold running water and set aside.

Wash the peaches and cut in half. Remove the pits and cut into bite-sized pieces. Set aside.

Cut the cantaloupe in half. Scoop out the seeds and flesh. Cut two wedges and peel them. Chop into chunks and set aside. Reserve the rest of the cantaloupe in a refrigerator.

Wash the carrot and cut into thick slices. Set aside.

Wash the apple and remove the core. Cut into bite-sized pieces and set aside.

Now, process blackberries, peaches, cantaloupe, carrot, and apple in a juicer. Transfer to serving glasses and stir in the water.

Add some ice cubes and serve immediately.

Nutritional information per serving: Kcal: 272, Protein: 7.7g, Carbs: 85g, Fats: 2.3g

20.   Artichoke Zucchini Juice

Ingredients:

1 large artichoke

1 medium-sized zucchini

1 large carrot

1 red leaf lettuce, torn

1 cup of watercress, torn

3 oz. of water

Preparation:

Trim off the outer leaves of the artichoke using a sharp knife. Cut into small pieces and set aside.

Peel the zucchini and cut in half. Scoop out the seeds and cut into chunks. Set aside. Set aside.

Wash the carrot and cut into thick slices. Set aside.

Combine red leaf lettuce and watercress in a colander. Wash under cold running water. Drain and torn with hands. Set aside.

Now, process artichoke, zucchini, carrot, red leaf lettuce, and watercress in a juicer. Transfer to serving glasses and stir in the water.

You can sprinkle with some fresh mint, but this is optional.

Add few ice cubes and serve immediately.

Nutritional information per serving: Kcal: 94, Protein: 9.4g, Carbs: 31.1g, Fats: 1.1g

21.   Orange Pomegranate Juice

Ingredients:

1 large orange

1 cup of pomegranate seeds

1 cup of purple cabbage, torn

1 cup of sweet potatoes, cubed

1 large cucumber

2 oz. of water

Preparation:

Peel the orange and divide into wedges. Set aside.

Cut the top of the pomegranate fruit using a sharp knife. Slice down to each of the white membranes inside of the fruit. Pop the seeds into a measuring cup and set aside.

Wash the cabbage thoroughly under cold running water. Drain and torn with hands. Set aside.

Peel the sweet potato and cut into cubes. Fill the measuring cup and reserve the rest for another juice. Set aside.

Wash the cucumber and cut into thick slices. Set aside.

Now, combine orange, pomegranate seeds, purple cabbage, sweet potatoes, and cucumber in a juicer and process until juiced.

Transfer to serving glasses and stir in the water. Add some ice cubes and serve immediately.

Nutritional information per serving: Kcal: 251, Protein: 6.8g, Carbs: 73.1g, Fats: 1.5g

22. Celery Grapefruit Juice

Ingredients:

2 cups of celery, chopped

2 large grapefruits

1 large lime

2 large carrots

1 ginger root slice, 1-inch

2 oz. of water

Preparation:

Wash the celery and chop into small pieces. About 2 large stalks will be enough. Set aside.

Peel the grapefruits and divide into wedges. Set aside.

Peel the lime lengthwise in half. Set aside.

Wash the carrots and cut into thick slices. Set aside.

Peel the ginger slice and set aside.

Now, process celery, grapefruits, lime, carrots, and ginger in a juicer. Transfer to serving glasses and stir in the water.

Refrigerate for 15 minutes before serving.

Enjoy!

Nutritional information per serving: Kcal: 250, Protein: 6.7g, Carbs: 76.3g, Fats: 1.4g

23.   Papaya Cantaloupe Juice

Ingredients:

1 cup of papaya, chopped

1 large green apple, cored

1 cup of cantaloupe, cubed

1 large cucumber

1 large lemon

Preparation:

Peel the papaya and cut lengthwise in half. Scoop out the black seeds and flesh using a spoon. Cut into small chunks and fill the measuring cup. Refrigerate the rest for some other juice recipe. Set aside.

Wash the apple and remove the core. Cut into bite-sized pieces and set aside.

Cut the cantaloupe in half. Scoop out the seeds and flesh. Cut two wedges and peel them. Chop into chunks and set aside. Reserve the rest of the cantaloupe in a refrigerator.

Wash the cucumber and cut into thick slices. Set aside.

Peel the lime and cut lengthwise in half. Set aside.

Now, process papaya, apple, cantaloupe, cucumber, and lime in a juicer. Transfer to serving glasses and add few ice cubes before serving.

Nutritional information per serving: Kcal: 245, Protein: 5.5g, Carbs: 72.8g, Fats: 1.6g

24.   Guava Squash Juice

Ingredients:

1 cup of butternut squash, chopped

1 large guava

1 large carrot

1 large cucumber

1 large orange

1 tbsp. of honey

Preparation:

Peel the butternut squash and remove the seeds using a spoon. Cut into small cubes and reserve the rest of the squash for some other recipe. Wrap in a plastic foil and refrigerate.

Peel the guava and cut into chunks. Set aside.

Wash the carrot and cucumber and cut into thick slices. Set aside.

Now, combine butternut squash, guava, carrot, and cucumber in a juicer and process until juiced.

Transfer to serving glasses and stir in the honey.

Add some ice and serve immediately.

Nutritional information per serving: Kcal: 266, Protein: 7.2g, Carbs: 80.7g, Fats: 1.4g

25.   Blueberry Melon Juice

Ingredients:

1 cup of fresh blueberries

2 cups of watermelon, cubed

1 large Granny Smith's apple

1 cup of Romaine lettuce, torn

3 oz. of coconut water

Preparation:

Wash the blueberries under cold running water. Drain and set aside.

Cut the watermelon lengthwise. For one cup, you will need about one large wedge. Peel and cut into chunks. Remove the seeds and set aside. Reserve the rest of the melon for some other juices.

Wash the lettuce thoroughly and torn with hands. Set aside.

Now, combine blueberries, watermelon, apple, and lettuce in a juicer and process until juiced. Transfer to serving glasses and stir in the coconut water.

Add few ice cubes and serve immediately.

Nutritional information per serving: Kcal: 282, Protein: 4.4g, Carbs: 77g, Fats: 1.4g

26.   Lemon Basil Juice

Ingredients:

2 large lemons

2 cups of fresh basil, torn

1 medium-sized orange

1 large cucumber

1 small ginger knob, 1-inch

2 oz. of water

Preparation:

Peel the lemons and cut lengthwise in half. Set aside.

Wash the basil leave thoroughly under cold running water. Drain and set aside.

Peel the orange and divide into wedges. Set aside.

Wash the cucumber and cut into thick slices. Set aside.

Peel the ginger root knob and set aside.

Now, combine lemons, basil, orange, cucumber, and ginger in a juicer and process until juiced.

Transfer to serving glasses and stir in the water.

Refrigerate for 20 minutes before serving, or add some ice and serve immediately.

Note:

Lemon contains a high amount of citrate, so make sure to add more water than usual.

Nutritional information per serving: Kcal: 124, Protein: 6.1g, Carbs: 39.5g, Fats: 1.1g

27. Swiss Chard Carrot Juice

Ingredients:

3 large carrots

2 cups of Swiss chard

1 cup of cauliflower

1 large lime

1 large orange

2 oz. of water

Preparation:

Wash the carrots and cut into thick slices. Set aside.

Wash the Swiss chard thoroughly and torn with hands. Set aside.

Trim off the outer leaves of cauliflower. Wash it and cut into small pieces. Fill the measuring cup and reserve the rest in the refrigerator.

Peel the lime and cut lengthwise in half. Set aside.

Peel the orange and divide into wedges. Set aside.

Now, process carrots, Swiss chard, cauliflower, lime, and orange in a juicer. Transfer to serving glasses and stir in the water.

Add some ice and serve immediately.

Nutritional information per serving: Kcal: 173, Protein: 7.3g, Carbs: 54g, Fats: 1.2g

28.   Red Bell Pepper Beet Juice

Ingredients:

3 large beets, trimmed

2 large red bell peppers, chopped

1 cup of fresh basil

1 large lime

1 cup of red leaf lettuce, torn

 1 large cucumber

Preparation:

Wash the beets and trim off the green parts. Cut into small pieces and set aside.

Wash the red bell peppers and cut in half. Remove the seeds and roughly chop it. Set aside.

Peel the lime and cut lengthwise in half. Set aside.

Place the red leaf lettuce in a colander and wash thoroughly under cold running water. Drain and torn with hands. Set aside.

Wash the cucumber and cut into thick slices. Set aside.

Now, process beets, red bell peppers, lime, red leaf lettuce, and cucumber in a juicer. Transfer to serving glasses and add few ice cubes.

Serve immediately.

Nutritional information per serving: Kcal: 208, Protein: 10.5g, Carbs: 59.2g, Fats: 1.9g

29.   Kiwi Kale Juice

Ingredients:

3 large kiwis

1 cup of fresh kale

1 large lemon

1 large green apple, cored

1 cup of fresh mint

A handful of fresh spinach

3 oz. of water

Preparation:

Peel the kiwis and lemon. Cut lengthwise in half and set aside.

Wash kale, mint, and spinach and combine in a large bowl. Pour hot water enough to cover the ingredients. Let it soak for 10 minutes. Drain and torn with hands. Set aside.

Wash the apple and remove the core. Cut into bite-sized pieces and set aside.

Now, process kiwis, lemon, kale, mint, spinach, and apple in a juicer. Transfer to serving glasses and stir in the water.

Add some ice and serve immediately.

Nutritional information per serving: Kcal: 246, Protein: 8.6g, Carbs: 74.5g, Fats: 2.6g

30.   Leek Radish Juice

Ingredients:

2 large leeks, chopped

3 large radishes, chopped

2 cups of beet greens, torn

1 cup of collard greens, torn

1 large cucumber

½ tsp of Himalayan salt

¼ tsp of Cayenne pepper, ground

3 oz. of water

Preparation:

Wash the leeks and chop into small pieces. Set aside.

Wash the radishes and trim off the green parts. Cut in half and set aside.

Combine beet greens and collard greens in a colander. Wash thoroughly under cold running water. Drain and set aside.

Wash the cucumber and cut into thick slices. Set aside-

Now, combine leeks, radishes, beet greens, collard greens, and cucumber in a juicer and process until juiced.

Transfer to serving glasses and stir in the salt, Cayenne pepper, and water.

Refrigerate for 15 minutes before serving.

Enjoy!

Nutritional information per serving: Kcal: 148, Protein: 7.6g, Carbs: 42.3g, Fats: 1.2g

31. Fuji Cranberry Juice

Ingredients:

1 cup of cranberries

1 large orange

1 cup of watermelon, cubed

1 small Fuji apple, cored

1 small ginger knob, 1-inch

2 oz. of coconut water

Preparation:

Place the cranberries in a colander and wash under cold running water. Drain and set aside.

Peel the orange and divide into wedges. Set aside.

Cut the watermelon lengthwise. For one cup, you will need about 1 large wedge. Peel and cut into chunks. Remove the seeds and set aside. Reserve the rest of the melon for some other juices.

Wash the apple and remove the core. Cut into bite-sized pieces and set aside.

Peel the ginger root knob and set aside.

Now, combine cranberries, orange, watermelon, apple, and ginger in a juicer and process until juiced.

Transfer to serving glasses and stir in the coconut water. Add some ice and serve immediately.

Enjoy!

Nutritional information per serving: Kcal: 223, Protein: 3.8g, Carbs: 66g, Fats: 0.9g

32.   Avocado Pineapple Juice

Ingredients:

1 cup of avocado, cubed

1 cup of pineapple chunks

1 large orange

1 large cucumber

2 oz. of water

Preparation:

Peel the avocado and cut in half. Remove the pit and cut into small cubes. Set aside.

Cut the top of a pineapple and peel it using a sharp knife. Cut into small chunks. Reserve the rest of the pineapple in a refrigerator.

Peel the orange and divide into wedges. Set aside.

Wash the cucumber and cut into thick slices. Set aside.

Now, combine avocado, pineapple, orange, and cucumber in a juicer and process until juiced.

Transfer to serving glasses and stir in the water. Add few ice cubes and serve immediately.

Nutritional information per serving: Kcal: 375, Protein: 7.5g, Carbs: 66.6g, Fats: 22.15g

33.   Agave Plum Juice

Ingredients:

5 large plums, pitted

1 large Granny Smith apple, cored

1 cup of watermelon, diced

1 tbsp. of agave nectar

3 oz. of water

Preparation:

Wash the plums and cut in half. Remove the pits and cut into small pieces. Set aside.

Wash the apple and remove the core. Cut into bite-sized pieces and set aside.

Cut the watermelon lengthwise. For one cup, you will need about 1 large wedge. Peel and cut into chunks. Remove the seeds and set aside. Reserve the rest of the melon for some other juices.

Now, combine plums, apple, and watermelon in a juicer and blend until juiced.

Transfer to serving glasses and stir in the agave nectar and water. Add some ice and serve.

Nutritional information per serving: Kcal: 330, Protein: 4.1g, Carbs: 93.2g, Fats: 1.5g

34.   Cauliflower Beet Juice

Ingredients:

1 small cauliflower head, chopped

2 large beets, trimmed

1 large lime

2 large radishes, chopped

¼ tsp of Himalayan salt

3 oz. of water

Preparation:

Trim off the outer leaves of cauliflower. Wash it and cut into small pieces. Set aside.

Wash the beets and radishes. Trim off the green parts and cut into bite-sized pieces. Set aside.

Peel the lime and cut lengthwise in half. Set aside.

Now, combine cauliflower, beets, radishes, and lime in a juicer. Transfer to serving glasses and stir in the Himalayan salt and water.

Add some ice cubes and serve immediately.

Nutritional information per serving: Kcal: 135, Protein: 9.3g, Carbs: 41g, Fats: 1.2g

35. Green Beans Carrot Juice

Ingredients:

1 cup of green beans

3 large carrots

1 large lemon

1 cup of fresh kale, torn

1 large cucumber

1 tbsp. of honey, raw

Preparation:

Wash the green beans and place them in a medium pot. Add water enough to cover and soak for at least 2 hours. Set aside.

Wash the carrots and cut into thick slices. Set aside.

Wash the kale thoroughly under cold running water. Drain and set aside.

Now, process green beans, carrots, lemon, kale, and cucumber in a juicer.

Transfer to serving glasses and stir in the honey. Refrigerate for 30 minutes and serve.

Enjoy!

Nutritional information per serving: Kcal: 239, Protein: 9.4g, Carbs: 50g, Fats: 1.8g

36.   Brussels Sprout Cabbage Juice

Ingredients:

2 cups of Brussels sprouts, halved

1 cup of green cabbage, torn

1 large zucchini, chopped

1 cup of celery, chopped

¼ tsp of Himalayan salt

2 oz. of water

Preparation:

Wash the Brussels sprouts and trim off the outer leaves. Cut in half and set aside.

Wash the cabbage thoroughly under cold running water. Drain and torn with hands. Set aside.

Peel the zucchini and cut in half. Scoop out the seeds and chop into small pieces. Set aside.

Wash the celery and cut into small pieces. Set aside.

Now, combine Brussels sprouts, cabbage, zucchini, and celery in a juicer and process until juiced. Transfer to serving glasses and stir in the Himalayan salt and water.

Add few ice cubes or refrigerate before serving.

Nutritional information per serving: Kcal: 115, Protein: 11.7g, Carbs: 33.9g, Fats: 1.8g

37.   Mixed Squash Juice

Ingredients:

1 cup of butternut squash, chopped

1 cup of crookneck squash, chopped

1 large zucchini

1 cup of pumpkin, chopped

1 large carrot

¼ tsp of Himalayan salt

2 oz. of water

Preparation:

Peel the butternut squash and remove the seeds using a spoon. Cut into small cubes and reserve the rest of the squash for some other recipe. Wrap in a plastic foil and refrigerate.

Wash the crookneck squash and cut in half. Scoop out the seeds using a spoon. Cut into small chunks and set aside. Reserve the rest for another juice.

Peel the zucchini and cut in lengthwise in half. Scrap out the seeds and cut into chunks. Set aside.

Peel the pumpkin and cut in half. Scoop out the seeds using a spoon. Cut one large wedge and peel it. Cut into small chunks and set aside. Reserve the rest for later.

Wash the carrot and cut into thick slices. Set aside.

Now, process butternut squash, crookneck squash, zucchini, pumpkin, and carrot in a juicer.

Transfer to serving glasses and stir in the Himalayan salt and water. Refrigerate for 15 minutes before serving.

Enjoy!

Nutritional information per serving: Kcal: 163, Protein: 8.4g, Carbs: 45.8g, Fats: 1.8g

38.   Blackberry Cantaloupe Juice

Ingredients:

2 cups of blackberries

1 cup of cantaloupe, diced

1 large orange

1 large lemon

1 small Granny Smith apple

Preparation:

Place the blackberries in a colander and wash under cold running water. Drain and set aside.

Cut the cantaloupe in half. Scoop out the seeds and flesh. Cut two wedges and peel them. Chop into chunks and set aside. Reserve the rest of the cantaloupe in a refrigerator.

Peel the orange and divide into wedges. Set aside.

Peel the lemon and cut lengthwise in half. Set aside.

Wash the apple and remove the core. Cut into bite-sized pieces and set aside.

Now, combine blackberries, cantaloupe, orange, lemon, and apple in a juicer and process until juiced. Transfer to serving glasses and refrigerate for 10 minutes before serving.

Nutritional information per serving: Kcal: 258, Protein: 8.3g, Carbs: 87g, Fats: 2.4g

39.   Peach Apple Juice

Ingredients:

2 large peaches, chopped

1 medium-sized red apple, cored

1 large orange

1 ginger root knob, 1-inch

2 oz. of water

Preparation:

Wash the peaches and cut in half. Remove the pits and cut into small pieces. Set aside.

Wash the apple and remove the core. Cut into bite-sized pieces and set aside.

Peel the orange and divide into wedges. Set aside.

Peel the ginger root knob and set aside.

Now, process peaches, apple, orange, and ginger in a juicer. Transfer to serving glasses and stir in the water.

Add some ice or refrigerate before serving.

Nutritional information per serving: Kcal: 294, Protein: 5.6g, Carbs: 85.8g, Fats: 1.5g

40.   Carrot Watermelon Juice

Ingredients:

3 large carrots

1 large green apple, cored

1 large orange

1 cup of watermelon, diced

1 cup of green grapes

1 small ginger root knob, 1-inch

Preparation:

Wash the carrots and cut into thick slices. Set aside.

Wash the apple and remove the core. Cut into bite-sized pieces and set aside.

Peel the orange and divide into wedges. Set aside.

Cut the watermelon lengthwise. For one cup, you will need about 1 large wedge. Peel and cut into chunks. Remove the seeds and set aside. Reserve the rest of the melon for some other juices.

Wash the grapes under cold running water. Drain and set aside.

Peel the ginger root knob and set aside.

Now, combine carrots, apple, orange, watermelon, grapes, and ginger in a juicer and process until juiced.

Transfer to serving glasses and add some ice before serving.

Enjoy!

Nutritional information per serving: Kcal: 335, Protein: 6.2g, Carbs: 98g, Fats: 1.7g

41.   Broccoli Arugula Juice

Ingredients:

1 cup of broccoli

1 cup of arugula, torn

2 large leeks, chopped

1 cup of beet greens, torn

1 cup of collard greens, torn

1 large cucumber

1 large lime

A handful of spinach, torn

Preparation:

Combine arugula, beet greens, collard greens, and spinach in a colander. Wash under cold running water and torn with hands.

Wash the broccoli and cut into small chunks. Set aside.

Wash the leeks and cut into small pieces. Set aside.

Wash the cucumber and cut into thick slices. Set aside.

Peel the lime and cut lengthwise in half. Set aside.

Now, process arugula, beet greens, collard greens, spinach, leeks, broccoli, cucumber, and lime in a juicer. Transfer to serving glasses and refrigerate for 30 minutes before serving.

Enjoy!

Nutritional information per serving: Kcal: 194, Protein: 13.1g, Carbs: 55.7g, Fats: 1.8g

42.   Cranberry Mango Juice

Ingredients:

1 cup of cranberries

1 cup of mango chunks

1 medium-sized green apple, cored

1 large honeydew melon wedge, chopped

1 cup of fresh mint

½ cup of hot water

Preparation:

Place the cranberries in a colander and wash under cold running water. Drain and set aside.

Peel the mango and cut into chunks. Set aside.

Wash the apple and remove the core. Cut into bite-sized pieces and set aside.

Cut the honeydew melon lengthwise in half. Scoop out the seeds using a spoon. Cut the large wedges and peel them. Cut into small chunks and place in a bowl. Wrap the rest of the melon in a plastic foil and refrigerate.

Combine mint with hot water and let it stand for 15 minutes.

Now, process mango, apple, honeydew melon, and mint in a juicer. Transfer to serving glasses and add water from the soaked mint. Refrigerate for 30 minutes before serving.

Nutritional information per serving: Kcal: 261, Protein: 4.3g, Carbs: 79.1g, Fats: 1.5g

43.   Celery Avocado Juice

Ingredients:

3 cups of celery, chopped

1 cup of avocado chunks

1 cup of cantaloupe, chopped

1 cup of fresh basil, torn

1 cup of cucumber, sliced

2 oz. of water

Preparation:

Wash the celery and cut into small pieces. Set aside.

Peel the avocado and cut in half. Remove the pit and cut into chunks. Fill the measuring cup and refrigerate the rest for some other juice.

Cut the cantaloupe in half. Scoop out the seeds and flesh. Cut two wedges and peel them. Chop into chunks and set aside. Reserve the rest of the cantaloupe in a refrigerator.

Wash the basil thoroughly under cold running water. Drain and torn with hands. Set aside.

Wash the cucumber and cut into thick slices. Set aside.

Now, process celery, avocado, cantaloupe, basil, and cucumber in a juicer. Transfer to serving glasses and refrigerate for 15 minutes before serving.

Enjoy!

Nutritional information per serving: Kcal: 288, Protein: 7.5g, Carbs: 37.1g, Fats: 23g

44.   Grapefruit Raspberry Juice

Ingredients:

1 large grapefruit

1 cup of raspberries

1 large lemon

1 large lime

1 medium-sized yellow apple, cored

4 oz. of coconut water

Preparation:

Peel the grapefruit and divide into wedges. Set aside.

Place the raspberries in a colander and wash under cold running water. Drain and set aside.

Peel the lemon and lime. Cut lengthwise in half and set aside.

Wash the apple and remove the core. Cut into bite-sized pieces and set aside.

Now combine grapefruit, raspberries, lemon, lime, and apple in a juicer and process until juiced. Transfer to serving glasses and stir in the coconut water.

Add some ice and serve immediately.

Note:

Lemon and lime contain a high amount of citrate, so make sure to add more water than usual.

Nutritional information per serving: Kcal: 240, Protein: 4.6g, Carbs: 76g, Fats: 1.6g

45.   Sweet Artichoke Juice

Ingredients:

1 large artichoke

1 large green apple, cored

1 cup of mustard greens, torn

1 large honeydew melon wedge

1 cup of watercress, torn

2 oz. of water

¼ tsp of agave nectar

Preparation:

Trim off the outer leaves of the artichoke using a sharp knife. Cut into bite-sized pieces and set aside.

Wash the apple and remove the core. Cut into bite-sized pieces and set aside.

Cut the honeydew melon lengthwise in half. Scoop out the seeds using a spoon. Cut one large wedge and peel it. Cut into small chunks and place in a bowl. Wrap the rest of the melon in a plastic foil and refrigerate.

Combine watercress and mustard greens in a colander and wash under cold running water. Drain and set aside.

Now, process artichoke, apple, honeydew melon, watercress, and mustard greens in a juicer. Transfer to serving glasses and stir in the water and agave nectar.

Add some ice and serve immediately.

Nutritional information per serving: Kcal: 261, Protein: 9.4g, Carbs: 79.6g, Fats: 1.1g

46.   Guava Melon Juice

Ingredients:

1 large guava

1 cup of watermelon

1 large orange

1 large kiwi

1 large green apple, cored

3 oz. of coconut water

Preparation:

Wash the guava and cut into chunks. If you are using large fruit, reserve the rest for some other recipe in a refrigerator.

Cut the watermelon lengthwise. For one cup, you will need about one large wedge. Peel and cut into chunks. Remove the seeds and set aside. Reserve the rest of the melon for some other juices.

Peel the orange and divide into wedges. Set aside.

Peel the kiwi and cut lengthwise in half. Set aside.

Wash the apple and remove the core. Cut into bite-sized pieces and set aside.

Now, combine guava, watermelon, orange, kiwi, and apple in a juicer and process until juiced. Transfer to serving glasses and stir in the coconut water.

Add some ice or refrigerate before serving.

Enjoy!

Nutritional information per serving: Kcal: 264, Protein: 5.6g, Carbs: 73.8g, Fats: 1.6g

47.   Cherry Blueberry Juice

Ingredients:

1 cup of cherries, pitted

1 large green apple, cored

1 cup of blueberries

1 medium-sized orange

3 oz. of coconut water

1 tbsp. of agave nectar

Preparation:

Combine cherries and blueberries in a colander. Wash under cold running water. Drain and set aside.

Wash the apple and remove the core. Cut into bite-sized pieces and set aside.

Peel the orange and divide into wedges. Set aside.

Now, combine cherries, blueberries, apple, and orange in a juicer and process until juiced. Transfer to serving glasses and stir in the coconut water.

Add few ice cubes and serve immediately.

Enjoy!

Nutritional information per serving: Kcal: 375, Protein: 4.8g, Carbs: 91.5g, Fats: 1.3g

48.   Fennel Rosemary Juice

Ingredients:

1 large fennel

1 large Granny Smith apple

1 large cucumber

1 rosemary sprig

¼ tsp of Himalayan salt

2 oz. of water

Preparation:

Wash the fennel bulb and trim off the wilted outer layers. Cut into small chunks and set aside.

Wash the apple and remove the core. Cut into bite-sized pieces and set aside.

Wash the cucumber and cut into thick pieces. Set aside.

Now, process fennel, apple, and cucumber in a juicer. Transfer to serving glasses and stir in the Himalayan salt and water. Sprinkle with rosemary and refrigerate for 30 minutes before serving.

Enjoy!

Nutritional information per serving: Kcal: 179, Protein: 5.7g, Carbs: 56g, Fats: 1.2g

49.   Strawberry Orange Juice

Ingredients:

1 cup of strawberries

1 large orange

1 cup of cantaloupe

1 large carrot

2 oz. of water

Preparation:

Wash the strawberries under cold running water. Drain and cut in half. Set aside.

Peel the orange and divide into wedges. Set aside.

Cut the cantaloupe in half. Scoop out the seeds. Cut two wedges and peel them. Chop into chunks and set aside. Reserve the rest of the cantaloupe in a refrigerator.

Wash the carrot and cut into thick slices. Set aside.

Now, combine strawberries, orange, cantaloupe, and carrot in a juicer and process until juiced.

Transfer to serving glasses and stir in the water. Add some ice and serve immediately.

Nutritional information per serving: Kcal: 177, Protein: 4.9g, Carbs: 55g, Fats: 1.2g

50.   Orange Cauliflower Juice

Ingredients:

1 cup of cauliflower, chopped

1 large orange

1 large carrot

1 large red bell pepper

1 cup of fresh kale, torn

¼ tsp of Himalayan salt

3 oz. of water

Preparation:

Trim off the outer leaves of a cauliflower. Wash it and cut into small pieces and fill the measuring cup. Reserve the rest in the refrigerator.

Peel the orange and divide into wedges. Set aside.

Wash the carrot and cut into thick slices. Set aside.

Wash the red bell pepper and cut in half. Remove the seeds and cut in small pieces. Set aside.

Wash the kale thoroughly and torn with hands. Set aside.

Now, process cauliflower, orange, carrot, red bell pepper, and kale in a juicer. Transfer to serving glasses and stir in the salt and water.

Refrigerate for 10 minutes before serving.

Enjoy!

Nutritional information per serving: Kcal: 169, Protein: 8.9g, Carbs: 49.6g, Fats: 1.8g

51.   Plum Tomato Juice

Ingredients:

5 plum tomatoes, halved

1 cup of watercress, torn

1 cup of basil, torn

1 large green bell pepper

1 large cucumber

A handful of spinach

Preparation:

Wash the plum tomatoes and place them in a bowl. Cut in half and reserve the juice while cutting. Set aside.

Combine watercress, basil, and spinach in a colander. Wash thoroughly under cold running water. Drain and torn with hands. Set aside.

Wash the green bell pepper and cut in half. Remove the seeds and chop into small pieces. Set aside.

Wash the cucumber and cut into thick slices. Set aside.

Now, process plum tomatoes, watercress, basil, spinach, green bell pepper, and cucumber in a juicer. Transfer to serving glasses and stir in the salt and water.

Add some ice and serve.

Nutritional information per serving: Kcal: 112, Protein: 8.5g, Carbs: 32.7g, Fats: 1.5g

52.   Zucchini Beet Juice

Ingredients:

1 large zucchini

1 cup of beets, trimmed

1 large green apple

1 large radish, trimmed

1 large celery stalk, chopped

2 oz. of water

Preparation:

Peel the zucchini and cut in half. Scoop out the seeds and cut into small chunks. Set aside.

Wash the beets and radish. Trim off the green parts and cut into small pieces. Set aside.

Wash the apple and remove the core. Cut into bite-sized pieces and set aside.

Wash the celery and chop it into bite-sized pieces. Set aside.

Now, combine zucchini, beets, apple, radish, and celery in a juicer and process until juiced. Transfer to serving glasses and stir in the water.

Add few ice cubes before serving and enjoy!

Nutritional information per serving: Kcal: 170, Protein: 7.3g, Carbs: 47.9g, Fats: 1.7g

53. Cinnamon Pumpkin Juice

Ingredients:

1 cup of pumpkin chunks

1 large yellow apple, cored

1 large carrot

1 large orange

¼ tsp of cinnamon, ground

3 oz. of water

Preparation:

Peel the pumpkin and cut in half. Scoop out the seeds using a spoon. Cut one large wedge and peel it. Cut into small chunks and set aside. Reserve the rest for later.

Wash the carrot and cut into thick slices. Set aside.

Wash the apple and remove the core. Cut into bite-sized pieces and set aside.

Peel the orange and divide into wedges. Set aside.

Now, process pumpkin, apple, carrot, and orange in a juicer. Transfer to serving glasses and stir in the cinnamon and water.

Add few ice cubes and serve immediately.

Nutritional information per serving: Kcal: 220, Protein: 4.1g, Carbs: 65.3g, Fats: 0.8g

54.   Brussels Sprout Crookneck Squash Juice

Ingredients:

1 cup of Brussels sprouts

1 cup of crookneck squash

1 large cucumber

2 large kiwis

1 large lime

3 oz. water

1 tbsp. of honey

Preparation:

Wash the Brussels sprouts and trim off the outer layers. Cut in half and set aside.

Wash the crookneck squash and cut in half. Scoop out the seeds using a spoon. Cut into small chunks and fill the measuring cup. Reserve the rest for another juice.

Wash the cucumber and cut into thick slices. Set aside.

Peel the kiwis and lime. Cut lengthwise in half and set aside.

Now, combine Brussels sprouts, crookneck squash, cucumber, kiwis, and lime in a juicer and process until juiced.

Transfer to serving glasses and stir in the water and honey. Add some ice or refrigerate for 15 minutes before serving.

Enjoy!

Nutritional information per serving: Kcal: 221, Protein: 7.8g, Carbs: 64.6g, Fats: 1.7g

ADDITIONAL TITLES FROM THIS AUTHOR

70 Effective Meal Recipes to Prevent and Solve Being Overweight: Burn Fat Fast by Using Proper Dieting and Smart Nutrition

By

Joe Correa CSN

48 Acne Solving Meal Recipes: The Fast and Natural Path to Fixing Your Acne Problems in Less Than 10 Days!

By

Joe Correa CSN

41 Alzheimer's Preventing Meal Recipes: Reduce or Eliminate Your Alzheimer's Condition in 30 Days or Less!

By

Joe Correa CSN

70 Effective Breast Cancer Meal Recipes: Prevent and Fight Breast Cancer with Smart Nutrition and Powerful Foods

By

Joe Correa CSN

CPSIA information can be obtained
at www.ICGtesting.com
Printed in the USA
LVHW051714261119
638429LV00001B/148/P

9 781635 316896